Great Bands of the 90s

Exclusive Distributors:
Music Sales Limited
8-9 Frith Street,
London W1V 5TZ, England.
Music Sales Pty Limited
120 Rothschild Avenue,
Rosebery, NSW 2018,
Australia.

Order No. AM952370
ISBN 0-7119-7318-0
This book © Copyright 1999 by Wise Publications

Designed by Pearce Marchbank, Studio Twenty
Printed in the United Kingdom by Caligraving
Limited, Thetford, Norfolk.
Cover photographs courtesy of London Features
International and Rex Features.
Text photographs courtesy of London Features
International, except one or two where
the copyright owners were unreachable.
We would be grateful if the photographers
concerned would contact us.

Your Guarantee of Quality
As publishers, we strive to produce every
book to the highest commercial standards.
This book has been carefully designed to
minimise awkward page turns and to make
playing from it a real pleasure. Particular care
has been given to specifying acid-free,
neutral-sized paper made from pulps which
have not been elemental chlorine bleached.
This pulp is from farmed sustainable forests
and was produced with special regard for
the environment.
Throughout, the printing and binding have been
planned to ensure a sturdy, attractive publication
which should give years of enjoyment.
If your copy fails to meet our high standards,
please inform us and we will gladly replace it.

Music Sales' complete catalogue describes
thousands of titles and is available in full colour
sections by subject, direct from Music Sales
Limited. Please state your areas of interest and
send a cheque/postal order for £1.50 for postage
to: Music Sales Limited, Newmarket Road,
Bury St. Edmunds, Suffolk IP33 3YB.

www.internetmusicshop.com

Wise Publications
London/New York/Paris/Sydney/Copenhagen/Madrid

If the nineties are to be remembered for anything, it will probably be for pop music being reclaimed by teenagers - even if the people behind the music weren't universally of school age themselves.

In the nineties pop music was once again about fandom, and if a few hormonal youngsters could be relieved of their pocket money in the process, so much the better. That, after all, is the great tradition of the pop industry. Of four such old-fashioned teen-appeal bands featured in this volume, East 17 possess the longest history and the most interesting development...from urchin-like pretenders to Take That's throne, through the media infamy caused by apparent drug endorsement to today's smooth R&B combo. Stay Another Day catches them approximately midway through the cycle. Boyzone, meanwhile, survived the extraordinary decision to cover Cat Stevens' 'Father and Son' to conquer the bedroom walls of teenager central.

The Spice Girls brought us girl power, union jack dresses and smash hits like 2 Become 1. Suddenly it was inadequate for pop music fans to worship The Beatles and know their Buzzcocks b-sides. If you couldn't also tell the difference between Mel B and Mel C, your name wasn't on the list and you weren't coming in, Granddad. Most recently, All Saints have added a sassy kick to a well-worn but photogenic formula. They seem to be having fun, and Never Ever is as good a take on urban R&B as anything Puff Daddy or his ilk have exported from America.

Adult rock did not disappear altogether, even if some of its writers were obsessed by notions of youth and ageing. Two of the best songs of the decade, Pulp's righteous Common People and Manic Street Preachers' A Design For Life both addressed the dearth of opportunity and endless banality in everyday, working-class existence. After 10 years in the wilderness, Common People, a sanguine tale of inverted social climbing, finally fulfilled Jarvis Cocker's lifelong ambition to be a pop star. No-one has worn the crown with more endearing awkwardness. A Design For Life was memorably reviewed by one critic as 'millencholic'. Whatever, Manic Street Preachers have just as much reason as Cocker to feel vindicated by their new-found success.

Far more upbeat examples of nineties indie-pop come via Dodgy and The Lightning Seeds. The latter's Ian Broudie, producer to the stars, has enjoyed huge success through World Cup tie-ins and the patronage of middle-class CD racks the world's suburbs over. Good Enough was simply the best of several fine singles by Dodgy, a band who sadly bid farewell to planet pop within a couple of years of its release.

R&B to nineties audiences now meant a sound based on Motown and classic soul sides, infused with hip-hop rhythms and street rhymes, rather than the blues-based guitar rock it had once signified. The all-conquering Fugees were simply the most popular exponents of the new sound. Killing Me Softly is an intriguing new twist on a song

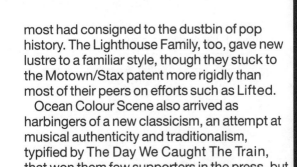

most had consigned to the dustbin of pop history. The Lighthouse Family, too, gave new lustre to a familiar style, though they stuck to the Motown/Stax patent more rigidly than most of their peers on efforts such as Lifted.

Ocean Colour Scene also arrived as harbingers of a new classicism, an attempt at musical authenticity and traditionalism, typified by The Day We Caught The Train, that won them few supporters in the press, but the enduring friendship of Paul Weller. The Seahorses' Blinded By The Sun saw John Squire finally move on from the ashes of The Stone Roses, while Everything But The Girl gravitated from bedroom acoustic angst to a new and unlikely role as drum 'n' bass heroes via Missing. Old stagers Wet Wet Wet regained their place in the nation's hearts when Goodnight Girl was featured on a *Coronation Street* Christmas special. In January 1992, it topped the charts for four weeks and gave the kiss of life to a group who looked likely to fade in the new decade.

New personalities emerged to replace fallen heroes. They have their detractors, but would not the world be a sadder place without Catatonia and their irrepressible mouthpiece Cerys? A band who were, say it softly, not ashamed of being Welsh, you got the distinct feeling Catatonia could also drink allcomers under the table. A welcome constant has been the satirical pen of Beautiful South mainman Paul Heaton, whose take on romance always derived more from Marx and Baudelaire than Mills And Boon. What next after Rotterdam? If anyone composes a heart-breaking ballad about a fictional flirtation in Scunthorpe, pound to a penny it will be the Beautiful South.

However, the definitive nineties band must surely be Oasis...the all-conquering great white hopes of Britpop, built on influences ranging from The Beatles to The Sex Pistols and The Stone Roses. The brothers Gallagher took their Mancunian predecessor's ambition and attitude and coupled them with a song-writing sensibility that struck a chord with music fans and the general public alike. Their popularity was built on the back of a string of classic singles, but it was Wonderwall, perhaps the group's quintessential song, which proved to be their breakthrough hit. A classic rock ballad featuring one of Liam's finest vocals, it remains firmly lodged in the nation's consciousness. *Alex Ogg*

2 Become 1

**Words & Music by Victoria Aadams,
Melanie Brown, Emma Bunton, Melanie
Chisholm, Geri Halliwell, Matt Rowe & Richard Stannard**

Verse 2:

Silly games that you were playing, empty words we both were saying,
Let's work it out boy, let's work it out boy.
Any deal that we endeavour, boys and girls feel good together,
Take it or leave it, take it or leave it.
Are you as good as I remember baby, get it on, get it on,
'Cause tonight is the night when two become one.

I need some love like I never needed love before, (wanna make love to ya baby.)
I had a little love, now I'm back for more, (wanna make love to ya baby.)
Set your spirit free, it's the only way to be.

Blinded By The Sun

Words & Music by Chris Helme

1. How would you feel— if I —— was to kneel— right down— at your feet?—
(Verse 2 see block lyric)

—— Right now is the way— it's go - ing to be— from

sun,_____ blind-ed by the sun._____

1. **2.**

I don't mean___ to sound___ un-kind_____ to you,—

___ you'll just have___ to go— and find___ some-thing else— to— do.—

Verse 2:
Who would you blame for blowing the flame right out?
Is it me? There is no doubt
I can do what I want to do
From now until forever.
Let's have less of getting clever with me.

You're wasting your time *etc.*

Common People

Music by Pulp
Lyrics by Jarvis Cocker

(Guitar solo 2nd time)

— a-bove— a shop— cut your hair— and get a job— smoke some fags—

— and play— some pool— pre-tend you nev-er went— to school,— but still you nev-

-er get it right— cos when you're laid— in bed— at night— watch-ing roa-

-ches climb— the wall,— if you called— your dad— he could stop— it all,— yeah.

Verse 2:
I took her to a supermarket
I don't know why but I had to start it somewhere
So it started there.
I said pretend you've got no money
But she just laughed and said
Oh, you're so funny, I said yeah?
(Spoken): Well I can't see anyone else smiling in here
Are you sure?

CHORUS:
You want to live like common people
You want to see whatever common people see
Want to sleep with common people
You want to sleep with common people like me.
But she didn't understand
She just smiled and held my hand.

Verse 3:
Guitar solo

CHORUS:
Sing along with the common people
Sing along and it might just get you through
Laugh along with the common people
Laugh along even though they're laughing at you
And the stupid things that you do
Because you think that poor is cool.

A Design For Life

Music by James Dean Bradfield & Sean Moore
Lyrics by Nicky Wire

for a shal - low piece of dig - ni - ty.

We don't talk a - bout love,

we on - ly want to get drunk, and we are not al -

Verses 2:
I wish I had a bottle
Right here in my dirty face,
To wear the scars
To show from where I came.

Verses 3:
I wish I had a bottle
Right here in my pretty face,
To wear the scars
To show from where I came.

The Day We Caught The Train

**Words & Music by Steve Cradock, Damon Minchella,
Oscar Harrison & Simon Fowler**

miles a - way. Roll a num - ber,

write an - oth - er song like Jim - my heard the day he caught the train.

Oh la la, oh la la.

Oh la la, oh la.

2. **A**

You and I should ride— the tracks— and find— our-selves— just wad-

D   **A**

-ing through— to-mor-row. And you and I when we're

com-ing down,— we're on-ly get-ting back— and you know— I feel— no sor-

D *(Vocal tacet 1º)* **A**   **G**   **Em**

-row. Oh— la la,— oh— la la.—

Oh_____ la la,_____ oh_____ la._____

Play 4 times,
then D.%. and fade

When you find that things— are get-ting wild, but don't— you want days like these.

Verse 2:
He sipped another rum and Coke and told a dirty joke.
Walking like Groucho, sucking on a number 10.
Rolling on the floor with the cigarette burns walked in
I'll miss the crush and I'm home again.
Stepping through the door
With the night in store, whiling just an hour away.
Step into the sky in the star bright feeling it's a brighter day.

A Different Beat

Words & Music by Martin Brannigan, Stephen Gately,
Ronan Keating, Shane Lynch & Ray Hedges

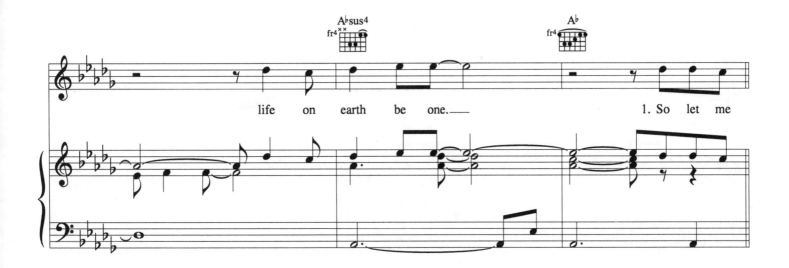

yea oh,___ ee - yea oh,___ ee - yea oh,___ by - yah..

___ (To a dif - fer - ent beat.) Ee - yea oh,___ ee - yea oh,___ ee -

yea oh,___ by - yah._____ 2. Hu - man - i -

I've seen the rain fall in Af - ri - ca,_____ I've touched the snows of A -

Verse 2:
Humanity has lost face,
Let's understand its grace,
Each day, one at a time,
Each life, including mine.

Let's take a stand and look around us now,
People,
So let's take a stand and look around us now,
People, oh people, oh people.

Good Enough

Words & Music by Nigel Clark, Mathew Priest & Andy Miller

1. I've got an ach-ing in my bones, I've been
(Verse 2 see block lyric)

ex - posed to what I want to see. The fuse is

Repeat ad lib. to fade

Verse 2:
Sing a song as the sun does rise,
If you don't ask questions
Then you don't know why.
There's a bridge to the other side,
Don't take your eyes from the prize.

Goodnight Girl

Words & Music by Graeme Clark, Tom Cunningham, Neil Mitchell & Marti Pellow

and do they have to know —
and I won't let them know —

a - bout my good - night girl. Caught up in your wish - ing well,

your hopes in - side it, — take your love and pro - mis - es and make them last, —

you make them last. 2. You

You

make them last. — Caught up in your wish - ing well, your hopes in - side it, —

Lifted

Words & Music by Paul Tucker, Emmanuel Baiyewu & Martin Brammer

But it ain't long be-fore I long___ for you___ like a

ray___ of hope com-ing through___ the blue._____

When it all gets dark and then___ the whole thing falls a-part,___ I guess___ it

does-n't real-ly mat-ter 'bout___ the rain, 'cause we'll get through it a-ny-way.

Verse 2:
It's undisturbable, the peace we've found
In a bright blue space up above the clouds.
Where everything is understandable,
You don't have to say anything too loud.

When our luck runs out again,
Brought back down to solid ground
I wouldn't say I'm mad about the rain
But we'll get through it anyway.
We'll get back to the stars again.

Killing Me Softly With His Song

Words by Norman Gimbel
Music by Charles Fox

Strum-ming my pain— with his fin— gers,— sing-ing my life— with his words,—

— kill-ing me soft - ly with his— song, kill-ing me soft-

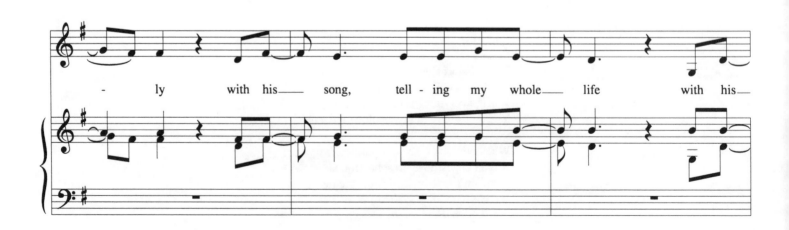

- ly with his— song, tell-ing my whole— life with his

words, kill - ing me soft - ly with his song.

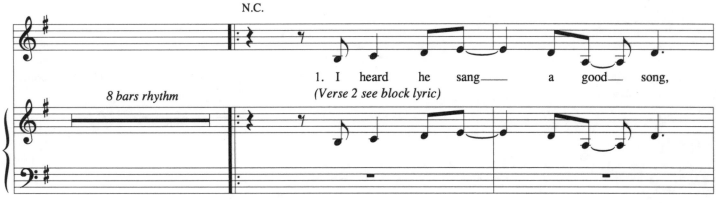

N.C.

8 bars rhythm

1. I heard he sang a good song,
(Verse 2 see block lyric)

I heard he had a smile, and so I came

to see him and lis - ten for a while,

and there he was,— this young boy, a strang-er to— my eyes.—

Em **Am** **D**

Strum-ming my pain— with his fin - gers,— (one time) sing-ing my life— with his words,—

G **Em** **A**

Spoken:
— (two times) kill-ing me soft - ly with his— song, kill-ing me soft -

D **C** **G**

- ly with his— song, tell-ing my whole— life with his—

la _____ woh _____ la _____

la. _____

Strum-ming my pain ____ with his fin - gers, _____ sing-ing my life ____ with his words,

kill-ing me soft - ly with his ____ song, kill-ing me soft -

54

Verse 2:
I felt all flushed with fever,
Embarrassed by the crowd,
I felt he found my letters
And read each one out loud,
I prayed that he would finish
But he just kept right on...

Marvellous

Words & Music by Ian Broudie

op - en up the win - dow and jump____ in - to____ the blue.____

Things____ could be mar - vel - lous soon.____

Oh, well these are the days,____ and this is the life,____

____ there'll al - ways be some - thing on____ your mind____ you'll ne - ver quite

find. Won't you ev - er make your mind up?

Oh you hate to hit till you hit the top,

op - en up the win - dow and jump in - to the blue.

Things could be mar - vel - lous,

things could be fa - bu - lous, soon.

1. Oh, well these are the days, and this is the life, there'll al - ways be some-
2. Now you'll ne - ver be sure if this is the time, if this is the mo -

4° To Coda ✛

Missing

Music by Ben Watt
Words by Tracey Thorn

1. I step off___ the train,___ I'm walk-ing down___ your street___
(Verses 2&3 see block lyric)

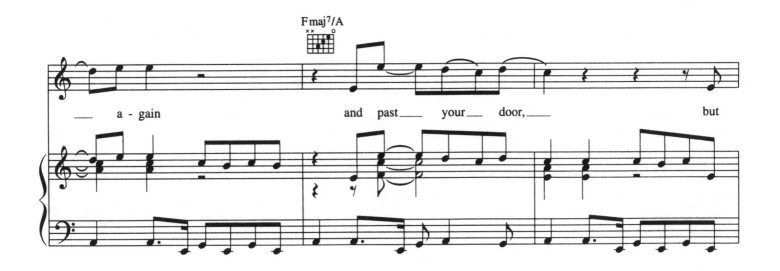

___ a - gain and past___ your___ door,___ but

you don't live___ there an - y - more. It's years since you've___ been there,___

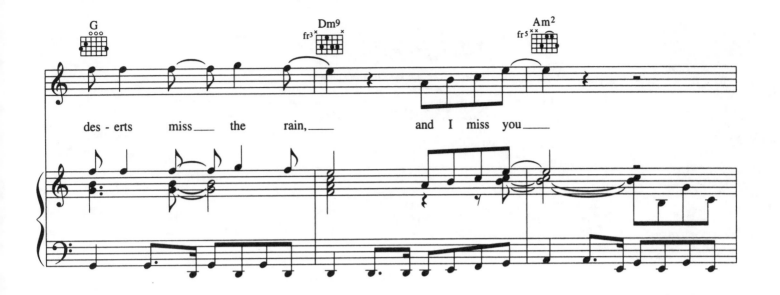

des - erts miss___ the rain,___ and I miss you___

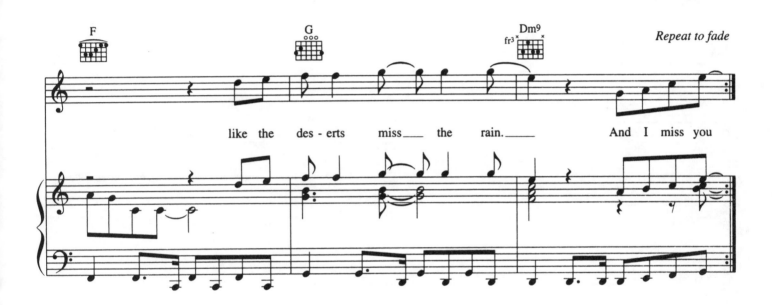

Repeat to fade

like the des - erts miss___ the rain.___ And I miss you

Verse 2:
Could you be dead?
You always were two steps ahead of everyone
We'd walk behind while you would run
I look up at your house
And I can almost hear you shout down to me
Where I always used to be
And I miss you.

Verse 3:
Back on the train
I ask why did I come again?
Can I confess I've been hanging 'round your old address
And the years have proved
To offer nothing since you moved
You're long gone but I can't move on
And I miss you.

Never Ever

Words & Music by Shaznay Lewis
Music by Rickidy Raw

(Spoken) A few questions that I need to know, how you could ever hurt me so, I need to know what I've done wrong, and how long it's been going on. Was it that I never paid enough attention, or did I not give enough affection? Not only will your answers keep me sane, but I'll know never to make the same mistake again. You can tell me to my face

find peace of mind, the hap-py mind, I once owned_____ yeah.

Flex-in' vo-cab-u-la-ry runs right through me. The al-pha-bet runs right from A to Z.

Con-ver-sa-tions, hes-i-ta-tions in___ my mind, you got my con-science ask-ing ques-tions that I can't find

I'm not cra-zy.___ I'm sure I ain't done no-thing wrong.___ No,

71

Verse 2:
I keep searching deep within my soul
For all the answers, don't wanna hurt no more.
I need peace, got to feel at ease, need to be
Free from pain, go insane, my heart aches.

Sometimes vocabulary runs through my head
The alphabet runs right from A to Z
Conversations, hesitations in my mind.
You got my conscience asking questions that I can't find
I'm not crazy
I'm sure I ain't done nothing wrong
Now I'm just waiting
'Cause I heard that this feeling won't last that long.

Road Rage

Words & Music by Cerys Matthews & Mark Roberts

If all you've got to do ___ to-day ___ is find ___ peace of mind, ___

come 'round you can take a piece ___ of mine. ___

And ___ if all you've got to do ___ to-day ___ is ___ he - si - tate, ___

Rotterdam

Words & Music by Paul Heaton & David Rotheray

long in___ Ir - ish stout.___ The

(1, 3.) whole place is pick-led, the peo - ple are pick - les for sure, and

no one knows if they done more here than they ev - er would do in a

jar._____ This could be

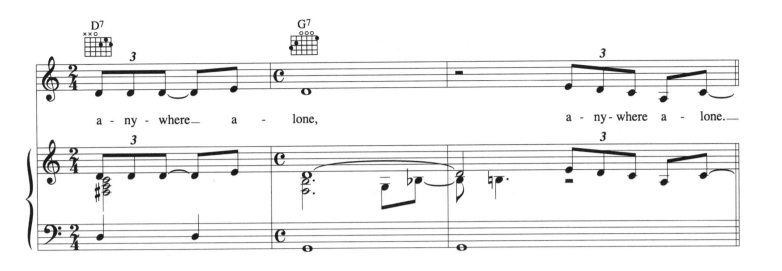

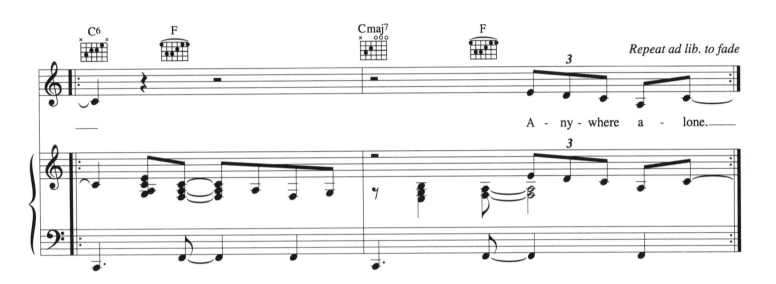

Verse 2:
And everyone is blonde
And everyone is beautiful.
And when blonde and beautiful are multiple
They become so dull and dutiful.
And when faced with dull and dutiful
They fire a warning flare,
Pedal khaki personality
With red underwear.

Stay Another Day

Words & Music by Mortimer, Kean & Hawken

Ba - by if you've got to go___ a - way,___ don't think I can take the pain___

— won't you stay a - no - ther day.___

Oh don't leave me a - lone — like this — don't you say it's the fi - nal kiss, —

Play 1° only

— won't you stay an - oth - er day. —

Play 2° only

Don't you know — we've come — too far — now, just to go —
(Verse 2 see block lyric)

and try to throw it all a-way.

Thought I heard you say you love me, that your love

was gon-na be here to stay.

I've on-ly just be-gun to know you, all I can say

is won't you stay— just one more day.—

2.

Ba - by if you've got to go— a - way,— don't think I can take the pain—

— won't you stay an - oth - er day.—

Verse 2:

I touch your face while you are sleeping
And hold your hand
Don't understand what's going on
Good times we had return to haunt me
Though it's for you
All that I do seems to be wrong.